KT-513-465

mrs Bailey

A catalogue record for this book is available
from the British Library

TM & © 1998 DreamWorks
Published by Ladybird Books Ltd
A subsidiary of the Penguin Group
A Pearson Company

LADYBIRD and the device of a Ladybird are trademarks of
Ladybird Books Ltd Loughborough Leicestershire UK

All rights reserved. No part of this publication may be reproduced,
stored in a retrieval system, or transmitted in any form or by any means,
electronic, mechanical, photocopying, recording or otherwise,
without the prior consent of the copyright owner.

THE PRINCE OF EGYPT

Adapted by Audrey Daly

Ladybird

Long, long ago in Egypt, the Hebrew slaves were full of fear. The Pharaoh's guards were everywhere, snatching baby boys from their mothers' arms. In one home Yocheved held her little son Moses close to her heart. He was in great danger, but she was sure God would keep him safe. When the way was clear, she took Moses and her older children Miriam and Aaron and fled to the river. Tears welled up in Yocheved's eyes as she put her baby in a basket. She sang him a lullaby, then set him adrift on the water. Miriam watched and saw the basket come to rest in the palace water garden. The Queen herself picked up Moses. In the years that followed, she brought him up with her own son, Rameses, as a prince of Egypt.

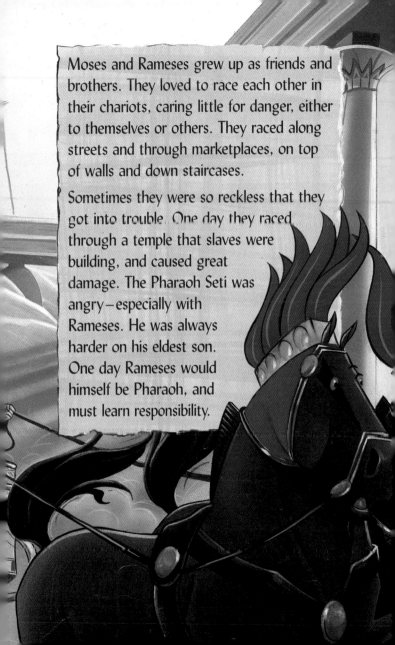

Moses and Rameses grew up as friends and brothers. They loved to race each other in their chariots, caring little for danger, either to themselves or others. They raced along streets and through marketplaces, on top of walls and down staircases.

Sometimes they were so reckless that they got into trouble. One day they raced through a temple that slaves were building, and caused great damage. The Pharaoh Seti was angry—especially with Rameses. He was always harder on his eldest son. One day Rameses would himself be Pharaoh, and must learn responsibility.

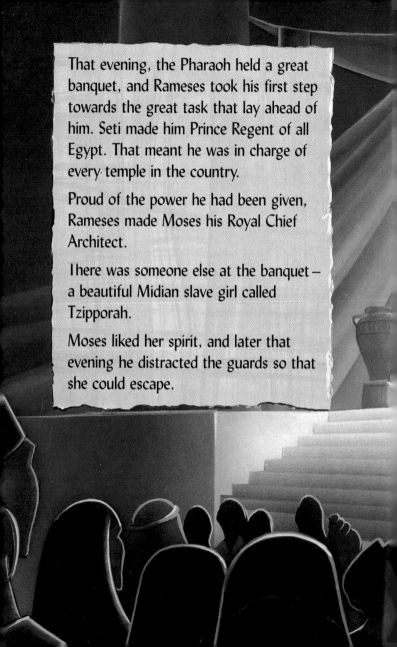

That evening, the Pharaoh held a great banquet, and Rameses took his first step towards the great task that lay ahead of him. Seti made him Prince Regent of all Egypt. That meant he was in charge of every temple in the country.

Proud of the power he had been given, Rameses made Moses his Royal Chief Architect.

There was someone else at the banquet – a beautiful Midian slave girl called Tzipporah.

Moses liked her spirit, and later that evening he distracted the guards so that she could escape.

Curious, Moses followed Tzipporah into the part of town where the slaves lived. When he turned the corner, there she was, getting water from two Hebrew slaves, Miriam and Aaron.

Miriam had been waiting for this moment. "I knew you would come back one day," she said. "I knew you cared about our freedom."

Moses was puzzled. "Freedom?" he asked. "Why should I care about your freedom?"

Miriam went on, "You are our deliverer. You are no prince of Egypt; you are our brother. Our mother set you adrift in a basket to save your life."

Moses' face grew black with anger. "You go too far. You shall be punished!"

Miriam made one last attempt. She began to sing a lullaby – the one that their mother had once sung. As Moses listened, something stirred deep within him. Confused, he turned and ran home to the palace.

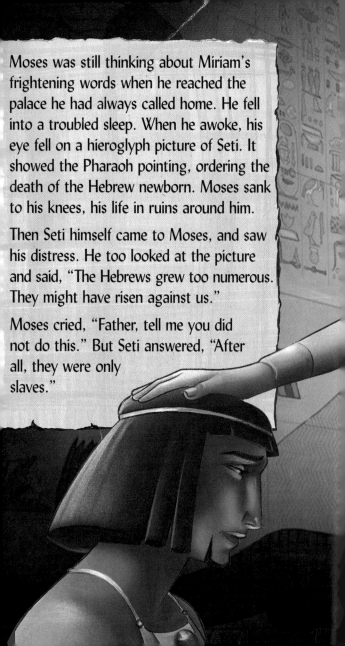

Moses was still thinking about Miriam's frightening words when he reached the palace he had always called home. He fell into a troubled sleep. When he awoke, his eye fell on a hieroglyph picture of Seti. It showed the Pharaoh pointing, ordering the death of the Hebrew newborn. Moses sank to his knees, his life in ruins around him.

Then Seti himself came to Moses, and saw his distress. He too looked at the picture and said, "The Hebrews grew too numerous. They might have risen against us."

Moses cried, "Father, tell me you did not do this." But Seti answered, "After all, they were only slaves."

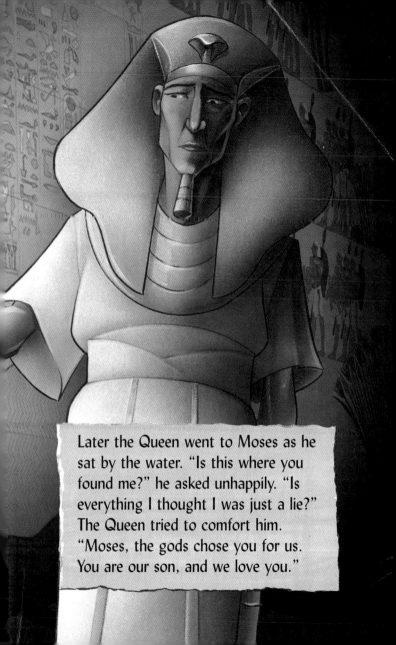

Later the Queen went to Moses as he sat by the water. "Is this where you found me?" he asked unhappily. "Is everything I thought I was just a lie?" The Queen tried to comfort him. "Moses, the gods chose you for us. You are our son, and we love you."

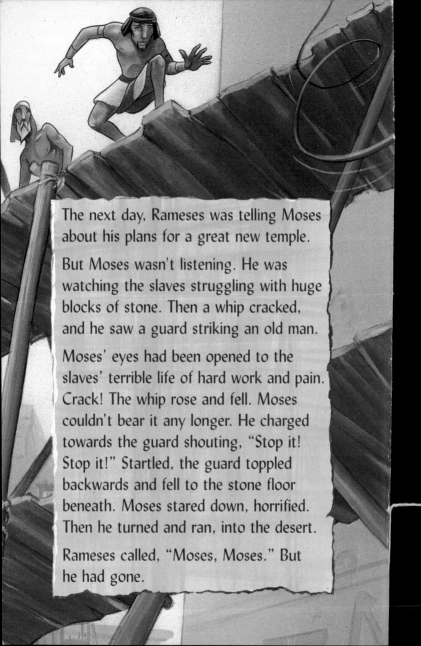

The next day, Rameses was telling Moses about his plans for a great new temple.

But Moses wasn't listening. He was watching the slaves struggling with huge blocks of stone. Then a whip cracked, and he saw a guard striking an old man.

Moses' eyes had been opened to the slaves' terrible life of hard work and pain. Crack! The whip rose and fell. Moses couldn't bear it any longer. He charged towards the guard shouting, "Stop it! Stop it!" Startled, the guard toppled backwards and fell to the stone floor beneath. Moses stared down, horrified. Then he turned and ran, into the desert.

Rameses called, "Moses, Moses." But he had gone.

As Moses tramped across the desert sand, he thought about his past life as a prince of Egypt. He thought about how happy he had been—and how uncaring. Slowly Moses sank further and further into despair.

And he began to grow thirstier and thirstier. Then a lone camel wandered past. It was Gamalu, Tzipporah's camel, although Moses didn't know it. With the last of his strength, he grabbed the waterbag on its side. Gamalu dragged Moses through the desert and to a well. There he met Tzipporah again. Her father Jethro gave a feast in his honour.

As time passed, Moses learned to be a part of the community, and his life as a shepherd was peaceful. His liking for Tzipporah grew into love, and they were married.

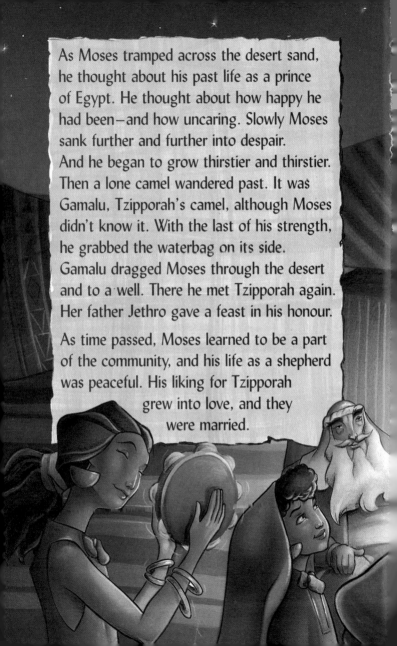

Early one morning, Moses heard a sheep's bell tinkling in the distance. One of his flock had wandered off. He followed the sound into a rocky canyon, and there he stopped, amazed. In front of him a small bush was on fire, yet it was not consumed. Moses pushed his staff into the flames, then drew it back, unchanged. He put his hand there – and it was unharmed.

As he stood there puzzled, a voice said, "Moses – Moses – Moses!" "Who are you?" asked Moses. "I am your God and the God of your ancestors," said the voice. "I shall send you unto Pharaoh to deliver my people out of slavery to their promised land."

"Who am I to lead these people?" asked Moses. "They won't listen to me." "Pharaoh himself will not listen," said God. "But I will stretch out my hand and smite Egypt. Take the staff in your hand, Moses. With it you shall do my wonders." The glow faded, and Moses went back to Tzipporah. "I must do God's work," he said. "I'm coming with you," said his wife.

When Moses and Tzipporah returned to Egypt, they found a new Pharaoh on the throne—but Moses knew him well. It was Rameses!

At first Rameses was overjoyed to see Moses. But when he found out why Moses had come, he wasn't pleased at all. "So you have returned only to free the Hebrews?" he said. "God commands that you let His people go," was Moses' reply. "Commands?" said Rameses angrily.

"Behold the power of God," said Moses. He threw his staff down and it turned into a snake.

The Pharaoh's magicians just laughed, and showed some tricks of their own. They too produced snakes.

The watching crowd enjoyed the show. When it was over, Rameses said grimly, "I do not know your God, and I will not let your people go."

As he spoke, unseen by all, Moses' snake ate the magicians' snakes, one by one.

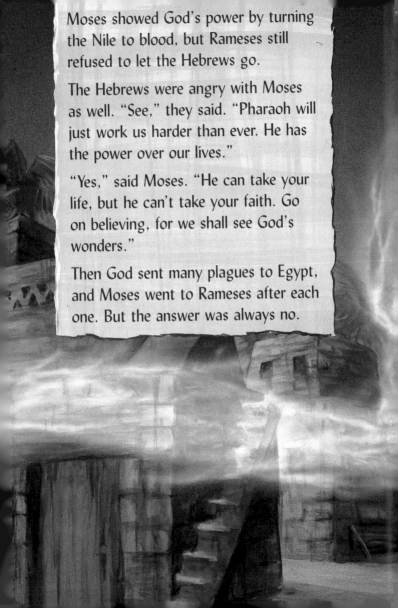

Moses showed God's power by turning the Nile to blood, but Rameses still refused to let the Hebrews go.

The Hebrews were angry with Moses as well. "See," they said. "Pharaoh will just work us harder than ever. He has the power over our lives."

"Yes," said Moses. "He can take your life, but he can't take your faith. Go on believing, for we shall see God's wonders."

Then God sent many plagues to Egypt, and Moses went to Rameses after each one. But the answer was always no.

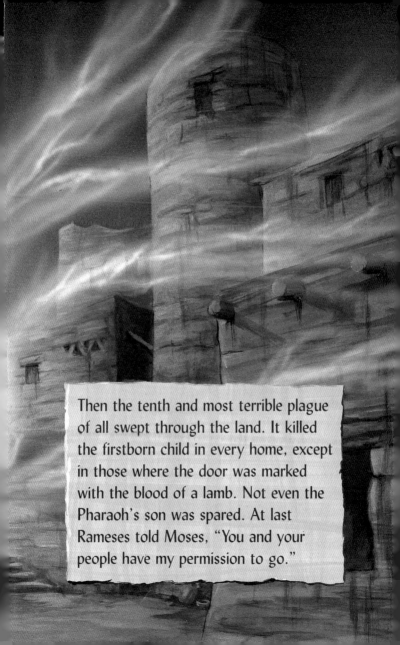

Then the tenth and most terrible plague of all swept through the land. It killed the firstborn child in every home, except in those where the door was marked with the blood of a lamb. Not even the Pharaoh's son was spared. At last Rameses told Moses, "You and your people have my permission to go."

So Moses led hundreds of thousands of Hebrews out of Egypt. When they reached the Red Sea and looked back, they could see the Egyptian army on its way. The Hebrews were in despair. Then a pillar of fire exploded from the water, separating them from the soldiers. Moses walked forward and placed his staff in the sea. God performed a miracle once more. The waters of the Red Sea parted so that the Hebrews could walk through safely.

The path was muddy and rough and everyone was frightened. Moses, Miriam and Tzipporah urged them on, helping where they could. Then the pillar of fire disappeared and the army came after them. But when the Egyptian soldiers were only halfway, the waters rushed together again, and the army was no more. And at that moment, Moses, the last Hebrew to cross, reached the opposite shore.

The Hebrews hugged one another. "We're free!" they shouted joyfully.

But, for a moment, Moses stood alone, looking back over the water. He was thinking of Rameses. Once they had been friends and brothers.

Then Tzipporah spoke. "Look at your people, Moses. They are free!"

He turned and looked upon the land and all his people. With his staff raised high, he walked forward, into the Promised Land.